Sharing the Harvest with Granddaddy Tenpenny

MARTY RAY GORDON

ILLUSTRATIONS BY: BONNIE SHIELDS

ISBN 979-8-88751-566-3 (paperback)
ISBN 979-8-88751-567-0 (digital)

Christian Faith Publishing
832 Park Avenue
Meadville, PA 16335
www.christianfaithpublishing.com

Printed in the United States of America

To my aunt Rachel and cousin Angela Arnold Hayes and in memory of Uncle Clayton Arnold. The unconditional love they showed me is a testament that the Spirit of Jesus always lived in them. Providing food and a roof over my head for many days of my life is just one of the many examples of sharing what they had with me. Cousin Angela Arnold Hayes always loved me as her only brother. Her willingness to follow me at a young age gave me the confidence to lead and share with others. Many life lessons I experienced with these family members shaped me and gave me guidance on who I wanted to be like and who I wanted to become.

Granddaddy Ray Tenpenny taught me valuable lessons about sharing, teamwork, mules, and family. I loved spending time with him on the farm in Wartrace, Tennessee, and I treasure the memories of working with the mules, planting potatoes, or just relaxing and watching baseball together.

In the summer of 1972, when I was twelve years old, Granddaddy purchased a pair of red sorrel john mules named Mike and Spike. With their flaxen tails and mane, they looked like twins. Granddaddy used an L-shaped wooden stick to measure the four-year-old mules. He placed one end of the measuring stick above the mule's shoulder and the other end on the ground. The stick was marked in hands, with each hand measuring four inches. Mike and Spike measured fifteen hands.

3

I remember many happy moments spent with Mike and Spike. Some memories take me back to calm summer days on Granddaddy's farm. But it wasn't always calm and quiet that summer.

Mike and Spike worked as a team. Granddaddy and I worked together to prepare them for the harness.

"Good job," Granddaddy said when I brushed the dust off the mules' slick red hair while he cleaned out their hooves. We did this preparation every time before putting on the harness. Once the harness was on, I led the team of mules to the wagon and backed them in position.

Granddaddy hooked the trace chains to the wagon's single trees. The single trees were made of wood about thirty-two inches long and had a hook on each end. The center of the single tree was pinned to the wagon. One end of the trace chains was connected to the collar on the mule, and the other end was connected to the single tree. The trace chains allowed the mules to pull the wagon forward.

Mike and Spike pulled together. This team of mules could do it all: pulling the slide, plowing the garden, and pulling the wagon. Spike, the lead mule, listened to Granddaddy's commands.

"Gee, Spike," Granddaddy said, and Spike turned right. Mike followed.

Granddaddy held the leather lines connected to the bridles and started testing the team's wagon-backing skills. The barn hall was ten feet wide and sixty feet long. The wagon was six feet wide, leaving two feet on each side. Without hesitation, the team started backing on Granddaddy's commands. The sorghum cane on the wagon needed to be unloaded at the back of the barn.

Granddaddy talked to the team.

"Back, Spike."

"Back, Mike."

"Pull up."

"Get over."

I was watching one side, and Granddaddy was watching the other side to ensure the wagon did not hit the wall. Within a few minutes, the wagon was at the back of the barn so the cane could be unloaded. This team passed the test and was very good at working together.

Mike was a good riding mule, too. Mike and I explored the area together, and Queenie, our dog, often joined us. I would ride Mike very fast in the tall grassy hayfields. Queenie would run along beside Mike, down to the creek, and across the other side. Mike was eager to go anywhere I steered him. Mike became my favorite mule.

One hot July day, the town of Wartrace was holding a fiddlers' convention and craft fair. After all the chores were done, I rode Mike to the fiddlers' convention. Queenie, jumping up and down and running all around, was very excited to go, too. I rode Mike across the creek and through the hayfield to get to the convention. A lot of people were walking around, looking at the crafts, and listening to the music. The vendors had tents set up to display their crafts. Some people wanted to take a photo of me riding Mike. I was smiling big for all the photos. Many of the kids wanted to touch Mike and to pet Queenie. Mike, Queenie, and I liked all the attention.

The convention was at the old Wartrace high school baseball field. On the other side of the old high school building was a train track. Mike had never heard a train coming down the tracks before or the loud whistle.

Just before the train horn sounded, someone said, "That sure is a fine-looking mule."

Having a fiddlers' convention so close to a train track led to disruptions. When the conductor sounded the train horn, no one could hear the fiddles.

Mike took notice, with his ears at attention and head looking toward the old schoolhouse. The sound of the tracks rattling and the loud horn made Mike tremble with fear. Mike took off like a speeding bullet. People started diving out of the way to keep from getting run over.

"Ride him, boy," someone yelled at me.

Mike was running the bases backward, rounding third base, and heading for second base, where the biggest tent was set up. Without a saddle, it was very difficult for me to stay in the center of Mike's back. As Mike passed by the big tent, his back leg caught the tent's tie-down rope. The rope was wrapped around his leg, and Mike was headed for first base, dragging the tent.

The train was still rattling the tracks as it passed through the town. Mike made the turn at first base and headed to home plate, where the fiddle players were located.

A man yelled at me, "Where are you going?"

"Ask the mule, don't ask me," I yelled back.

The fiddlers didn't have enough time to gather up all their instruments. Mike jumped over some instruments but landed on one fiddle.

I was doing all I could to get Mike to stop, but nothing was working. With a tent behind and a fiddle case stuck on one foot, Mike turned, went across the pitcher's mound, and headed to the outfield.

Next came the creek bank. Mike jumped in the middle of the creek. I stayed on Mike, who was forging the creek, dragging a tent, and had a fiddle stuck on one foot. I was holding on for dear life. The next jump was on the other side and up the bank. The tent and fiddle box came off in the creek. Running with all his might, Mike headed down Tenpenny Lane on Granddaddy's farm, into the barn hall, and stopped. I got off Mike, thanking God we were safe.

The rest of that summer brought calmer days of working on the farm and spending time with family.

In the middle of August, we had to dig the potatoes that were planted in the spring. Early in the morning, Granddaddy and I hooked Mike and Spike to the bull-tongue plow.

The bull-tongue plow was used to bust the middle ground up and spread the potatoes on top of the ground so they could be picked up by hand and placed in buckets. Gathering potatoes fresh from the field with mules required hard work. Granddaddy invited family, neighbors, and friends to share in the harvest. Aunt Rachel and Cousin Angela came out with buckets in the hot sun. After filling most of the buckets, Granddaddy drove Mike and Spike back over the potato patch. More potatoes came out of the ground. It was a great harvest that many people would share.

Sharing what you have was a principle and an act of obedience to God that Granddaddy taught me.

Let them do good, that they be rich in good
works, ready to give, willing to share.

—1 Timothy 6:18 NKJV

ABOUT THE AUTHOR

Marty Ray Gordon is a believer of Jesus Christ, a husband, a father of two sons, and a granddaddy to Aubrey Raine Gordon. Born in 1960, Gordon spent most of his time growing up in Wartrace, Tennessee, around his granddaddy, Ray Tenpenny, who was a legendary walking horse trainer. Gordon's appreciation for mules began in his childhood. Family tradition of dedication, determination, and devotion taught Gordon to work hard and appreciate people, animals, and nature. During the winter of 2021, the Holy Spirit inspired Gordon to create a mule show and a bluegrass festival for charities and to write a series of children's books about the experiences he has had with mules. Without any prior experience of creating a festival or writing a book, Gordon thanks God for the opportunity.

CPSIA information can be obtained
at www.ICGtesting.com
Printed in the USA
BVHW090912310323
661518BV00003B/42

* 9 7 9 8 8 8 7 5 1 5 6 6 3 *